A LIFEBUILDER 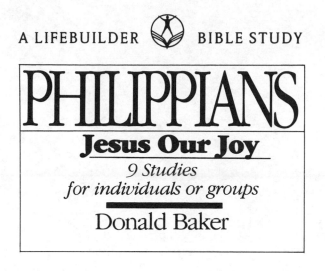 BIBLE STUDY

PHILIPPIANS

Jesus Our Joy

9 Studies
for individuals or groups

Donald Baker

SCRIPTURE UNION
130 City Road, London EC1V 2NJ

© 1985 Inter-Varsity Christian Fellowship of the United States of America
First published in the United States by InterVarsity Press
First published in Great Britain by Scripture Union, 1986
Reprinted 1987, 1988, 1989, 1990, 1992, 1993

All Scripture quotations, unless otherwise indicated, are taken from the Holy Bible, New International Version, copyright © 1973, 1978, 1984 by International Bible Society, published by Hodder and Stoughton.

ISBN 0 86201 427 1

Cover photograph: Gary Irving

Printed in England by Ebenezer Baylis & Son Limited, The Trinity Press, Worcester, and London

Contents

Getting the Most
from LifeBuilder Bible Studies

Many of us long to fill our minds and our lives with Scripture. We desire to be transformed by its message. LifeBuilder Bible Studies are designed to be an exciting, thought-provoking and challenging way to do just that. Their ultimate goal is to help us build our lives on God's Word.

How They Work

LifeBuilder Bible Studies have a number of distinctive features. Perhaps the most important is that they are *inductive* rather than *deductive*. In other words, they lead us to *discover* what the Bible says rather than simply *telling* us what it says.

They are also thought provoking. They help us to think about the meaning of the passage so that we can truly understand what the author is saying. The questions require more than one-word answers.

The studies are personal. Questions expose us to the promises, assurances, exhortations and challenges of God's Word. They are designed to allow the Scriptures to renew our minds so that we can be transformed by the Spirit of God. This is the ultimate goal of all Bible study.

The studies are versatile. They are designed for student, neighborhood and church groups. They are also effective for individual study.

How They're Put Together

LifeBuilder Bible Studies also have a distinctive format. Each study need take no more than forty-five minutes in a group setting or thirty minutes in personal study—unless you choose to take more time.

The studies can be used within a quarter system in a church and fit well in a semester or trimester system on a college campus. If a guide has more than thirteen studies, it is divided into two or occasionally three parts of approximately twelve studies each.

LifeBuilder Bible Studies use a workbook format. Space is provided for writing answers to each question. This is ideal for personal study and allows group members to prepare in advance for the discussion.

The studies also contain leader's notes. They show how to lead a group discussion, provide additional background information on certain questions, give helpful tips on group dynamics and suggest ways to deal with problems which may arise during the discussion. With such helps, someone with little or no experience can lead an effective study.

Suggestions for Individual Study

1. As you begin each study, pray that God will help you to understand and apply the passage to your life.

2. Read and reread the assigned Bible passage to familiarize yourself with what the author is saying. In the case of book studies, you may want to read through the entire book prior to the first study. This will give you a helpful overview of its contents.

3. A good modern translation of the Bible, rather than the King James Version or a paraphrase, will give you the most help. The New International Version, the New American Standard Bible and the Revised Standard Version are all recommended. However, the questions in this guide are based on the New International Version.

4. Write your answers in the space provided in the study guide. This will help you to express your understanding of the passage clearly.

5. It might be good to have a Bible dictionary handy. Use it to look up any unfamiliar words, names or places.

Suggestions for Group Study

1. Come to the study prepared. Follow the suggestions for individual study mentioned above. You will find that careful preparation will greatly enrich your time spent in group discussion.

2. Be willing to participate in the discussion. The leader of your group will not be lecturing. Instead, he or she will be encouraging the members of the group to discuss what they have learned from the passage. The leader will be asking the questions that are found in this guide. Plan to share what God has taught you in your individual study.

3. Stick to the passage being studied. Your answers should be based on the verses which are the focus of the discussion and not on outside authorities such as commentaries or speakers. This guide deliberately avoids jumping from book to book or passage to passage. Each study focuses on only one passage. Book studies are generally designed to lead you through the book in the order in which it was written. This will help you follow the author's argument.

4. Be sensitive to the other members of the group. Listen attentively when they share what they have learned. You may be surprised by their insights! Link what you say to the comments of others so the group stays on the topic. Also, be affirming whenever you can. This will encourage some of the more hesitant members of the group to participate.

5. Be careful not to dominate the discussion. We are sometimes so eager to share what we have learned that we leave too little opportunity for others to respond. By all means participate! But allow others to also.

6. Expect God to teach you through the passage being discussed and through the other members of the group. Pray that you will have an enjoyable and profitable time together.

7. If you are the discussion leader, you will find additional suggestions and helpful ideas for each study in the leader's notes. These are found at the back of the guide.

Introducing Philippians

"Rejoice in the Lord always," the author of Philippians exhorts us, "I will say it again: Rejoice!" Coming from most people, such words might sound trite and simplistic, but this is the apostle Paul speaking, a man who was not writing from a padded-leather office chair surrounded by books on how to be happy. On the contrary, he was a prisoner awaiting news that could result in his death. It isn't hard to get behind the words of Philippians and see the tension and uncertainty there. Yet through all this we see the example of a man whose life is filled with joy.

As we study Philippians, we discover Paul's secret: that a life lived for the glory of God will overflow with joy. What a message for our hurting world!

Philippi was an important city because it straddled the great east-west highway known as the Egnatian Way. The population of this city was cosmopolitan, being made up of Tracians, Greeks, Romans and a few Jews. In the center of the city was a large forum surrounded by temples, a library, fountains, monuments and public baths.

In 42 B.C. Antony and Octavia defeated Brutus and Cassius near Philippi. In honor of his victory, Antony made Philippi a Roman colony. This provided the Philippians with special rights and privileges as Roman citizens, and they responded with a great deal of pride and loyalty. Women enjoyed a high status in Philippi—taking an active part in both public and business life. Because of this, women also had important responsibilities in the Philippian church.

Paul founded this church sometime around the year A.D. 50, during his second missionary journey (Acts 16:12-40). From the letter to the Philippians, we learn that this church was taking its share of suffering (1:29), it was in some danger of division (1:27; 2:2; 4:2), it may have been leaning toward a doctrine of perfectionism (3:12-13), and it was threatened by the teaching of Judaizers—a group which insisted that all Christians adhere to Jewish laws and customs. But despite these problems, Paul's love for this church was obvious. He sincerely rejoiced at the progress they were making.

We know that Paul was writing to the Philippians from prison (1:12-14). Unfortunately, it is not clear which prison he was writing from. If he was writing during his imprisonment in Rome, then the letter can be dated sometime between A.D. 61-63. However, many scholars have pointed out that the conditions which Paul describes seem much harsher than what we know of the Roman imprisonment (Acts 28:16, 30-31). It could be that there was an earlier imprisonment not recorded in Acts. A good case has been made for Ephesus. If this is true, Philippians would have been written about A.D. 54.

Paul had several reasons for writing this letter. He wanted to explain why he was sending a man named Epaphroditus back to Philippi. He also wanted to thank the Philippians for the gift of money they had sent and to reassure his friends of his condition. Also, the news Paul had received concerning the Philippians made him long to encourage and advise a church he loved.

The purpose of this guide is to help you learn and apply Paul's secret to joyful living. This is done through nine studies, each taking about 30-45 minutes to complete. The first study looks at the founding of the Philippian church, introducing you to specific people to whom Paul wrote. The next seven studies help you get to the heart of Paul's teaching, taking one section at a time. The final study is not so much a review as a thematic overview, helping you recall and apply the points Paul felt were most important.

1
A Church
Is Born

Acts 16:6-40

Willliam Carey, the father of modern missions, once proposed
to a group of ministers that they discuss the implications of the Great
Commission. One minister retorted: "Young man, sit down. When God
pleases to convert the heathen, he will do it without your aid or mine!"
Fortunately, Carey did not share this man's imbalanced perspective. He
believed we should *expect* great things from God but also *attempt*
great things for God. This was also the view of Paul, Silas, Timothy and
Luke. In this passage we see them working together with God in
founding the Philippian church.

1. In what ways did God and people work together in your own
conversion?

2. Read Acts 16:6-40. What do verses 6-12 reveal about the way God
guided these missionaries to Philippi?

3. In verses 13-15 we are introduced to Lydia, the first convert. What human and divine factors led to her conversion?

4. Imagine that you had been present during the events described in verses 16-18. How would they have affected your view of these missionaries and Jesus Christ?

5. Verse 19 tells us that "the owners of the slave girl realized that their hope of making money was gone." What did they *fail* to realize about the significance of this event?

In what sense were the owners the real slaves in this story?

to Money.

6. Imagine that you are imprisoned with Paul and Silas (vv. 22-24). What sights, sounds and smells would you be experiencing? How would you feel?

7. How would your response to these circumstances compare with that of Paul and Silas (v. 25)?

Why do you think they responded as they did?

---

8. God not only caused an earthquake but also caused the prison doors to fly open and everybody's chains to come loose (v. 26). In what sense were these events an object lesson of the power of the gospel?

What effect did these events, together with the example of Paul and Silas, have on the jailer (vv. 27-34)?

The jailer & his family were saved.

---

9. How do Paul and Silas react when they are offered freedom (vv. 35-40)?

How might God have been using their imprisonment to help the new church?

10. This passage is a beautiful example of how the Spirit of God and the servants of God work together in evangelism. What specific prin ciples of evangelism can you learn from this passage?

In gods will. Vision.
Stunted. Filled lives. Readyness.
Obed. to the Spirit.. Know the word of Goc

How should these principles affect your evangelism?

2
Paul's Prayer
for the Philippians
Philippians 1:1-11

Have any of your good friends ever told you what they appreciate about you? Have you ever listened while others prayed for you? If so, you know what a warm feeling it is to be assured that others care. In Philippians 1:1-11 Paul prays and thanks God for his friends in Philippi. As you read the passage, try to imagine yourself sitting with Lydia, the jailer and their families as this letter is read for the first time.

1. Do you think our love and concern for others can be measured by how much we pray for them? Explain.

Prayer is important. but we have to show our love & concern.

2. Read Philippians 1:1-11. In verse 1 Paul describes himself as a servant of Christ Jesus. How was Paul's service to Christ and the Philippians evident in the previous study?

He was prepared to preach & suffer. & to build up people

3. What are Paul's feelings toward the Philippians (vv. 3-8)?

Parlmentary.

Why does he feel this way about them?

They are still his partners.

---

4. The previous study demonstrated how God "began a good work" in the Philippians (v. 6). Why would this give Paul confidence that God would also "carry it on to completion until the day of Christ Jesus"?

---

5. What do verses 3-8 reveal about healthy Christian relationships?

---

6. How can your present relationships be strengthened to become more like this?

Share & pray. with oneanother

---

7. What are Paul's prayer requests for the Philippians (vv. 9-11)?

That Love may abound.

8. Why would each of these qualities be essential to spiritual maturity?

9. What does Paul's prayer teach about how we should pray for others?

Depended. on each other.

10. Using Paul's prayer as a model, spend a few minutes thanking God and praying for someone you love in Christ.

3
A Joyful Imprisonment
Philippians 1:12-30

In this passage we discover that Paul is writing to the Philippians from prison. This puts a whole new perspective on the joyful mood of the letter. While Paul is writing, he is experiencing what most of us would describe as awful circumstances. Yet even at a time like this, Paul's first concern is that Christ is praised. This passage can teach us how to honor Christ in a difficult situation.

1. What people or things in life bring you the greatest joy? Explain why.

Family
Meeting other Christians
Visiting the sick.

2. Read Philippians 1:12-30. What does Paul say has happened as a result of his imprisonment (vv. 12-14)?

He encourages other people to speak out for the Lord. Courageously & fearlessly

3. Compare the motives of the two groups described in verses 15-18.

Preached out of envy & rivalry.

"   "   "   Love.

---

4. Have you ever been critical of the motives or methods of certain evangelists? If so, explain why.

~~Methods~~ Motives

How does your attitude compare to Paul's (vv. 15-18)?

---

5. What are Paul's considerations in choosing between life and death (vv. 20-26)?

So that others will see Christ

---

6. What does Paul mean when he says, "For to me, to live is Christ and to die is gain" (v. 21)?

7. To what extent have you adopted Paul's attitude toward life and death?

8. What does it mean to conduct ourselves in a manner worthy of the gospel (vv. 27-30)?

Standing form in one spirit encouraging one another.

9. Why is each of these attitudes or actions important, especially in the midst of suffering or persecution?

10. Look back over the passage. Then summarize the various factors which can transform difficult circumstances into a joyful, Christ-exalting situation.

Seeing Christ lifted up.
Prayers of Others

11. What are the most difficult circumstances you are presently facing?

Family

How can Christ be exalted in that situation?

4
The Path of Humility

Philippians 2:1-18

Is it possible to have a good self-image and still be humble? Can a person want to be the best without being conceited? In Philippians 2:1-18 Paul directs us to Jesus Christ, a person equal with God yet whose incarnation and life are the supreme example of humility. This passage urges us to imitate Christ's attitude.

1. What is the difference between humility and a poor self-image?

✓ S:

2. Read Philippians 2:1-18. How can our experience of Christ and his Spirit (v. 1) help us to achieve the unity Paul desires in verse 2?

3. How do verses 3-4 help us to understand the nature of humility?

Consern for others.
To be humbly. is to think of others

4. What does Paul mean when he says that Jesus "did not consider equality with God something to be grasped" (v. 6)?

5. How did each of Christ's actions illustrate humility and a concern for the interests of others (vv. 6-8)?

He was a Servant
Sexeyfise

6. In what areas of your life are you most tempted to be conceited or selfishly ambitious?

How can Christ's example challenge you to resist these temptations?

7. In your own words, describe God's response to Jesus' humility (vv. 9-11).

Because Jesus was humble God gave him a name above every name. He raised him to the highest place above.

How can God's response to Jesus help us when we are tempted to exalt ourselves rather than humble ourselves?

If we keep reminding ourselves of Jesus humble and how much more we need it.

---

8. In verses 12-13 Paul says you are to "work out your salvation" because God "works in you." How are these ideas related?

We must obey Him we must have fear and trembling to complete our Salvation Remembering that god is always at work in us to make us willing and able to obey His will for us.

9. How are we to be different from the "crooked and depraved generation" in which we live (v. 14-16)? *The world must see us differently by our love & caring & helping others we must remember not to complain or argue So that we can be children that God will be proud of. We must be shining lights for Him.*

10. Paul admits that he hopes to boast when Christ returns (v. 16). Why isn't this conceit? *Because he has done the work which gods had given him to do. and also recog that it was god. who equiped. him He will bost be cause what god has done in his life & through him.*

11. How is Paul himself an example of the principles described in this passage (vv. 16-18)?

---

12. Who might you be tempted to impress during the next few days? What act of humble service could you do for this person instead?

5
Servants
of Christ
Philippians 2:19-30

When the Philippians heard that Paul was in prison, they sent one of their members—a man named Epaphroditus—to Paul with a gift of money. It was his job to help Paul in any way necessary. Epaphroditus returned home carrying the letter to the Philippians.

In this section of the letter, Paul outlines his future plans and explains why he is sending Epaphroditus back. The passage gives several beautiful examples of Christian service as displayed in the lives of Timothy, Epaphroditus, Paul and the Philippians.

---

1. What do you enjoy most and least about serving others?

I enjoy serving People

---

2. Read Philippians 2:19-30. How is Timothy an example of the Christlike attitude considered in the previous study (vv. 19-23)?

1. Was a servant.

3. Why do you think people like Timothy are so rare (v. 20)?

No Time
Self.

4. Imagine that Timothy is being sent to visit your church or fellowship group. What might he do to help you?

encourage our faith:
"   us to work with oneanother.

5. Since Timothy won't be coming to visit, what are some practical ways you could follow his example?

Pray. encourage.

6. Why is Paul sending Epaphroditus back to Philippi (vv. 25-28)?

7. How is Christ's attitude evident in the relationships among Paul, Epaphroditus and the Philippians (vv. 25-30)?

8. Why is it important to honor people like Epaphroditus, especially in light of Christ's exaltation (2:9-11)?

9. Examine your plans and goals during the coming week. How can you bring your own interests into closer harmony with those of Jesus Christ?

10. What are some practical ways you can serve those around you during the coming week?

11. Pray that Christ will continue to give you the heart of a servant.

6
Rejoice in the Lord

Philippians 3:1-21

Have you ever become excited about an idea only to be deflated by the realities of making it work? Sometimes trying to live a Christian life is like that. We start off very excited about knowing the Lord, but it isn't long before the pressure of keeping "all the right rules" drains us of our joy. Unfortunately, we can then swing too far in the other direction and decide, "I'm not going to be concerned about Christian conduct. If Jesus has saved me, then it doesn't matter how I live." This attitude will destroy our joy as quickly as the first. So what is the solution? Paul tells us in this passage.

---

1. What are some of your most important goals in life?

Living a life pleasing to God.
Household Salvation

---

2. Read Philippians 3. How does rejoicing in the Lord (v. 1) differ from other reasons for joy?

Paul's past the ancountant. 1-11.   *(things used 11 times*

Paul the Alelect 12-16.

Paul's future the Celen 17-21.

Joy lasts when we Rejoice in the Lord.

3. Why were the people Paul warns against in verses 2-3 so danger-
ous?

all things through faith.
watch out for those who are against the Faith

4. Contrast Paul the Pharisee (vv. 4-6) with Paul the Christian (vv. 7-
11). How have his reasons for confidence changed?

from Confidence in the law to Confidence in Christ

5. How has knowing Christ turned his former profit into loss (v. 7)
and his outstanding credentials into rubbish (v. 8)?

Denifits Salavation

6. Have you ever placed your confidence in something, thinking it
would bring you closer to God, which you now consider to be rubbish? Explain.

7. In verse 6 Paul speaks of "legalistic righteousness." What legalisms
are today's Christians pressured to keep?

Handling money on a Sunday.

8. How do these legalisms get in the way of knowing Christ and rejoicing in the Lord?

9. How can each of the experiences described in verses 10-11 help us to know Christ better?

10. In verses 12-14 Paul compares himself to an athlete who is running a race. Why is this such an appropriate description of the Christian life?

What goal and prize is Paul straining to obtain?

11. To what extent do you think you have or have not taken Paul's view of the Christian life (vv. 12-16)?

12. In verses 17-21 Paul contrasts Christians with "enemies of the cross." What are the concerns and destiny of each group?

13. In verse 17 Paul asks us to follow his example. Summarize the ways in which he is an example to us in this chapter.

14. In what specific ways can you begin to follow Paul's example more fully?

7
Stand Firm in the Lord

Philippians 4:1-9

T *Family, Household Salvation*
Katerina' R.E. Children

ake a moment to think of the people you care most about. What is your greatest desire for these people? As Paul thinks of the Philippians, his greatest desire is that they will stand firm in what they have been taught. But he is also aware of some problems which may cause their faith to weaken. He writes to warn them that in order to stand firm they must put an end to disagreements, rejoice always and fill their thoughts with good things.

---

1. Read Philippians 4:1-9. Paul opens this chapter with the statement, "that is how you should stand firm in the Lord." Look back at 3:12-21. How are we to stand firm in the Lord?

---

2. Do you find your stand in the Lord to be firmer or weaker than it was a year ago? What has made the difference?

Firmer through the working of the Holy Spirit. Help from the group.

3. Why does Paul consider the Philippians his joy and crown?

4. Whom do you consider to be your joy and crown?

How does this affect your relationship with that person?

5. In verse 2 Paul pleads with Euodia and Syntyche "to agree with each other in the Lord." Why do you think he is so concerned about their relationship?

disrupt the whole fellowship,

6. What might someone like "loyal yokefellow" do to help these women (v. 3)?

7. What should be your response to disagreements within your church or fellowship group?

_____

8. What have you been anxious about recently?

_____

9. How can each of the promises and commands listed in verses 4-7 help you to be joyful, peaceful and free from anxiety?

_____

10. How can improper thoughts rob us of the peace God desires for us?

_____

11. How can true, noble, right, pure, lovely, admirable, excellent or praiseworthy thoughts help to cleanse our minds and restore our tranquility (v. 8)?

12. In verse 9 Paul tells us that the God of peace will be with us as we practice what we have learned. What have you learned in this passage that you need to put into practice?

8
Paul's Thank-You Note
Philippians 4:10-23

We've all written thank-you notes for gifts received for a birthday or for Christmas. Such notes usually include rather conventional phrases about the thankfulness of the recipient and the thoughtfulness of the giver. In Philippians 4 Paul thanks the Philippians for a gift of money they sent. However, it is a most unusual thank-you note. First he breaks the conventional rules by waiting until the very end of the letter to say thank you. Then he writes as though he didn't really need the gift!

1. Most Christians are strongly in favor of sending missionaries to other countries. Yet many missionaries have a difficult time raising their support. How would you explain this paradox?

2. Read Philippians 4:10-23. Paul thanks the Philippians not for the money but for the concern they have shown (v. 10). Why would this have been more important to Paul?

Money was not enfortain, Concern & prayer. is more enfaton

3. Many people believe they can only be content once they have reached a certain level of economic prosperity. How does their view differ from Paul's secret of contentment (vv. 11-13)?

To what extent have you learned to apply this secret?

4. How had the Philippians helped Paul both in the past and the present (vv. 14-18)?

Sharing in his troubles.

5. What opportunities do you have to meet the needs of those whose ministries require special support?

In the work of the church. & also outside outside the church. Prayer support.

6. What benefits does Paul expect the Philippians to receive from their giving (vv. 17-19)?

full credited in heaven

7. How can the promise of verse 19 encourage us to give to the needs of others?

_____

8. Many people complain that missionaries are always asking for money. How does this passage provide a model for both missionaries and those who support them?

_____

9. How will this passage affect your giving?

Give as you feel God guiding you.

9
Putting It All Together
Philippians 1—4

Studying a book like Philippians is similar to putting together a jigsaw puzzle. In previous studies we have looked in detail at the individual pieces. Now it is time to stand back and look at the completed puzzle. When we do this carefully, seemingly unrelated pieces suddenly become part of the overall picture.

1. What are the major themes Paul has emphasized in Philippians?

2. Paul uses the words *joy* and *rejoice* many times in Philippians. What causes him to rejoice (1:4, 18; 2:2, 17; 3:1; 4:1, 4, 10)?

3. How can Paul's example help you to rejoice even in adverse circumstances?

---

4. What principles have you learned:

—about living with meaning and purpose (1:20-26)?

—about living with a proper attitude toward yourself and others (2:1-11)?

—about the value of knowing Christ (3:4-11)?

—about living a peaceful and contented life (4:4-19)?

5. Modern authors have given us a great deal of advice on how to live a fulfilled life. In the light of what Paul tells us is worthwhile, how would you respond to the following quotes?

Each person's life is unique, separate from every other life. No one else can live your life, what you feel, get into your body and experience the world the way you do. It's the only life you get, and it's too precious to let others take advantage of it. Your functioning ought to bring you the joy of "pulling your own strings."[1]

Looking out for Number One is the conscious, rational effort to spend as much time as possible doing those things which will bring you the greatest amount of pleasure, and the less time on those which cause pain.[2]

You deserve to be rich, and you can be rich. *Moneylove* can help you have a life of abundance, filled with love and creativity and, incidentally, all the cash you want. It's as simple as this. Thinking rich will make you rich.[3]

---

6. In chapter 2 Paul sets forward the examples of Jesus Christ, Timothy, Epaphroditus and himself. What do they teach us about serving others?

How can a servant's attitude help us to promote and maintain Christian unity?

7. What changes have you observed in your life as a result of studying Philippians?

8. What have you enjoyed most about studying this letter?

[1]Wayne Dyer, *Pulling Your Own Strings* (New York: Avon, 1979).
[2]Robert J. Ringer, *Looking Out for Number One* (New York: Fawcett, 1978).
[3]Jerry Gillies, *Moneylove* (New York: Warner Books, 1979).

Leader's Notes

Leading a Bible discussion can be an enjoyable and rewarding experience. But it can also be *scary*—especially if you've never done it before. If this is your feeling, you're in good company. When God asked Moses to lead the Israelites out of Egypt, he replied, "O Lord, please send someone else to do it!" (Ex 4:13).

When Solomon became king of Israel, he felt the task was far beyond his abilities. "I am only a little child and do not know how to carry out my duties. . . . Who is able to govern this great people of yours?" (1 Kings 3:7, 9).

When God called Jeremiah to be a prophet, he replied, "Ah, Sovereign LORD, . . . I do not know how to speak; I am only a child" (Jer 1:6).

The list goes on. The apostles were "unschooled, ordinary men" (Acts 4:13). Timothy was young, frail and frightened. Paul's "thorn in the flesh" made him feel weak. But God's response to all of his servants—including you—is essentially the same: "My grace is sufficient for you" (2 Cor 12:9). Relax. God helped these people in spite of their weaknesses, and he can help you in spite of your feelings of inadequacy.

There is another reason why you should feel encouraged. Leading a Bible discussion is not difficult if you follow certain guidelines. You don't need to be an expert on the Bible or a trained teacher. The suggestions listed below should enable you to effectively and enjoyably fulfill your role as leader.

Preparing to Lead

1. Ask God to help you understand and apply the passage to your own life. Unless this happens, you will not be prepared to lead others. Pray too for the various members of the group. Ask God to give you an enjoyable and profitable time together studying his Word.

2. As you begin each study, read and reread the assigned Bible passage to familiarize yourself with what the author is saying. In the case of book studies, you may want to read through the entire book prior to the first study. This will give you a helpful overview of its contents.

3. This study guide is based on the New International Version of the Bible. It will help you and the group if you use this translation as the basis for your study and discussion. Encourage others to use the NIV also, but allow them the freedom to use whatever translation they prefer.

4. Carefully work through each question in the study. Spend time in meditation and reflection as you formulate your answers.

5. Write your answers in the space provided in the study guide. This will help you to express your understanding of the passage clearly.

6. It might help you to have a Bible dictionary handy. Use it to look up any unfamiliar words, names or places. (For additional help on how to study a passage, see chapter five of *Leading Bible Discussions,* IVP.)

7. Once you have finished your own study of the passage, familiarize yourself with the leader's notes for the study you are leading. These are designed to help you in several ways. First, they tell you the purpose the study guide author had in mind while writing the study. Take time to think through how the study questions work together to accomplish that purpose. Second, the notes provide you with additional background information or comments on some of the questions. This information can be useful if people have difficulty understanding or answering a question. Third, the leader's notes can alert you to potential problems you may encounter during the study.

8. If you wish to remind yourself of anything mentioned in the leader's notes, make a note to yourself below that question in the study.

Leading the Study

1. Begin the study on time. Unless you are leading an evangelistic Bible study, open with prayer, asking God to help you to understand and apply the passage.

2. Be sure that everyone in your group has a study guide. Encourage them to prepare beforehand for each discussion by working through the questions in the guide.

3. At the beginning of your first time together, explain that these studies are meant to be discussions not lectures. Encourage the members of the group to participate. However, do not put pressure on those who may be hesitant to speak during the first few sessions.

4. Read the introductory paragraph at the beginning of the discussion. This will orient the group to the passage being studied.

5. Read the passage aloud if you are studying one chapter or less. You may choose to do this yourself, or someone else may read if he or she has been asked to do so prior to the study. Longer passages may occasionally be read in parts at different times during the study. Some studies may cover several chapters. In such cases reading aloud would probably take too much time, so the group members should simply read the assigned passages prior to the study.

6. As you begin to ask the questions in the guide, keep several things in mind. First, the questions are designed to be used just as they are written. If you wish, you may simply read them aloud to the group. Or you may prefer to express them in your own words. However, unnecessary rewording of the questions is not recommended.

Second, the questions are intended to guide the group toward understanding and applying the *main idea* of the passage. The author of the guide has stated his or her view of this central idea in the *purpose* of the study in the leader's notes. You should try to understand how the passage expresses this idea and how the study questions work together to lead the group in that direction.

There may be times when it is appropriate to deviate from the study guide. For example, a question may have already been answered. If so, move on to the next question. Or someone may raise an important question not covered in the guide. Take time to discuss it! The important thing is to use discretion. There may be many routes you can travel to reach the goal of the study. But the easiest route is usually the one the author has suggested.

7. Avoid answering your own questions. If necessary, repeat or rephrase them until they are clearly understood. An eager group quickly becomes passive and silent if they think the leader will do most of the talking.

8. Don't be afraid of silence. People may need time to think about the question before formulating their answers.

9. Don't be content with just one answer. Ask, "What do the rest of you think?" or "Anything else?" until several people have given answers to the question.

10. Acknowledge all contributions. Try to be affirming whenever possible. Never reject an answer. If it is clearly wrong, ask, "Which verse led you to that conclusion?" or again, "What do the rest of you think?"

11. Don't expect every answer to be addressed to you, even though this will probably happen at first. As group members become more at ease, they will begin to truly interact with each other. This is one sign of a healthy discussion.

12. Don't be afraid of controversy. It can be very stimulating. If you don't resolve an issue completely, don't be frustrated. Move on and keep it in mind for later. A subsequent study may solve the problem.

13. Stick to the passage under consideration. It should be the source for answering the questions. Discourage the group from unnecessary cross-referencing. Likewise, stick to the subject and avoid going off on tangents.

14. Periodically summarize what the *group* has said about the passage. This helps to draw together the various ideas mentioned and gives continuity to the study. But don't preach.

15. Conclude your time together with conversational prayer. Be sure to ask God's help to apply those things which you learned in the study.

16. End on time.

Many more suggestions and helps are found in *Leading Bible Discussions* (IVP). Reading and studying through that would be well worth your time.

Components of Small Groups

A healthy small group should do more than study the Bible. There are four components you should consider as you structure your time together.

Nurture. Being a part of a small group should be a nurturing and edifying experience. You should grow in your knowledge and love of God and each other. If we are to properly love God, we must know and keep his commandments (Jn 14:15). That is why Bible study should be a foundational part of your small group. But you can be nurtured by other things as well. You can memorize Scripture, read and discuss a book, or occasionally listen to a tape of a good speaker.

Community. Most people have a need for close friendships. Your small group can be an excellent place to cultivate such relationships. Allow time for informal interaction before and after the study. Have a time of sharing during the meeting. Do fun things together as a group, such as a potluck supper or a picnic. Have someone bring refreshments to the meeting. Be creative!

Worship. A portion of your time together can be spent in worship and prayer. Praise God together for who he is. Thank him for what he has done and is doing in your lives and in the world. Pray for each other's needs. Ask God to help you to apply what you have learned. Sing hymns together.

Mission. Many small groups decide to work together in some form of outreach. This can be a practical way of applying what you have learned. You can host a series of evangelistic discussions for your friends or neighbors. You can visit people at a home for the elderly. Help a widow with cleaning or repair jobs around her home. Such projects can have a transforming influence on your group.

For a detailed discussion of the nature and function of small groups, read *Small Group Leaders' Handbook* or *Good Things Come in Small Groups* (both from IVP).

Study 1. A Church Is Born. Acts 16:6-40.

Purpose: From Acts 16 we can learn that God chooses people from many different backgrounds and builds them into one church. This study is intended to give an understanding of the people to whom Paul was writing. It also illustrates how God's Spirit and God's servants work together in evangelism.

Question 1. Almost every study begins with an "approach" question, which is meant to be asked *before* the passage is read. These questions are important for several reasons.

First, they help the group to warm up to each other. No matter how well a group may know each other or how comfortable they may be with each other, there is always a stiffness that needs to be overcome before people will begin to talk openly. A good question will break the ice.

Second, approach questions get people thinking along the lines of the topic of the study. Most people will have lots of different things going on in their minds (dinner, an important meeting coming up, how to get the car fixed) that will have nothing to do with the study. A creative question will get their attention and draw them into the discussion.

Third, approach questions can reveal where our thoughts or feelings need to be transformed by Scripture. This is why it is especially important *not* to read the passage before the approach question is asked. The passage will tend to color the honest reactions people would otherwise give because they are of course *supposed* to think the way the Bible does. Giving honest responses to various issues before they

find out what the Bible says may help them to see where their thoughts
or attitudes need to be changed.

Question 2. For this question it would be helpful to obtain a large
map of Paul's second missionary journey or to make copies of a map
for each participant. Group members should be encouraged to identify
on the map the places mentioned.

Verses 6-8 bring up the very interesting question of how the Holy
Spirit prevented Paul and his companions from preaching in Asia and
entering Bithynia. Unfortunately, the book of Acts doesn't give any
clues. It could have been an inward prompting, a prophecy given by
a Christian they encountered on the way or an external circumstance
such as bad weather. Whatever the means, Paul saw it as clear guidance
by the Holy Spirit. E. M. Blaiklock makes this interesting observation:

> These regions where Paul was forbidden to preach were not passed
> by in the progress of the gospel. There is evidence of very early
> foundations in Mysia, and for Bithynia there is the evidence of Pli-
> ny's famous letters. This Roman governor, writing sixty years later,
> speaks of the grip which Christianity had secured over his province,
> and of the measures of repression undertaken by him. (*The Acts of
> the Apostles* [Grand Rapids, Mich.: Eerdmans, 1959], p. 123)

Question 3. F. F. Bruce explains why Paul and his companions met
Lydia at the river:

> When Paul visited a new city, it was his practice to attend the local
> Jewish synagogue on the first sabbath after his arrival and seek an
> opportunity there for making the message known "to the Jew first".
> At Philippi, however, there does not appear to have been a syn-
> agogue. That can only mean that there were very few Jews in the
> place: had there been ten Jewish men, they would have sufficed to
> constitute a synagogue. No number of women could compensate
> for the absence of even one man necessary to complete the quorum
> of ten. There was, however, an unofficial meeting-place outside the
> city where a number of women—Jewesses and God-fearing Gen-
> tiles—came together to go through the appointed Jewish service of
> prayer for the sabbath day, even if they could not constitute a regular

synagogue congregation. (*The Book of Acts* [Grand Rapids, Mich.: Eerdmans, 1954], p. 331)

Question 4. It is important to realize that Paul was only the instrument of God in casting out the spirit from this slave girl. Jesus Christ is the one who actually cast it out. Once again, the human and the divine were working together.

Question 8. It is not at all unusual for Scripture to visually portray what is being taught. Jesus Christ claimed to be the bread of life (Jn 6:35) and fed the five thousand (Jn 6:1-15). He claimed to be the light of the world (Jn 9:5) and healed a blind man (Jn 9:6-12). The fact that God not only caused an earthquake but also caused *all* the prison doors to fly open and *everyone's* chains to come loose dramatically illustrates the power of the gospel to set people free.

Question 9. One of the reasons Acts was written was to prove that Christians were not trying to overthrow the Roman government. It shows Christians to be law-abiding citizens who are persecuted unjustly. By refusing to leave without a public apology, Paul and Silas forced the local officials to make an open proclamation that Christians who are Roman citizens have rights which must be upheld by the Roman law.

Study 2. Paul's Prayer for the Philippians. Philippians 1:1-11.
Purpose: To help people strengthen their Christian relationships through affirmation, godly affection and prayer.

Question 2. Although verse 1 states that the letter is from Paul and Timothy, it is obvious from the rest of the letter that Paul is really the one who is writing. Timothy's name was added because he was with Paul at the time and may have acted as his secretary. Questions in this and the rest of the studies are worded as if the letter came only from Paul.

Question 4. Paul's statement in verse 6 takes on new meaning when we reflect on how the Philippian church was founded. This would be a good time to briefly review those things which God did in bringing the church into being.

Study 3. A Joyful Imprisonment. Philippians 1:12-30.

Purpose: To help people deal with adversity in a way that brings honor to Christ. Paul serves as an excellent example because his great joy is so remarkable given his awful circumstances.

Question 3. The identity of those who "preach Christ out of envy and rivalry" (v. 15) is somewhat of a puzzle. Scholars seem to agree that they could not have been heretics who were taking advantage of Paul's imprisonment to teach false doctrine. Paul writes that he rejoices because "Christ is preached." If the preaching were heretical, Paul would never have made this statement. The envious preachers must have been Christians who personally disliked the apostle and hoped he would remain in prison. They probably saw the imprisonment as an opportunity to steal some of Paul's popularity and authority.

Question 6. People are often amazed that Paul is able to be joyful in the midst of such difficult circumstances. Yet verses 20-21 help us to understand the reason for his joy. If he were living merely for his own happiness and pleasure, then his joy would be senseless. But because he was living for Jesus Christ and the advancement of his kingdom, Paul had reason for joy: Jesus Christ was being preached and exalted because of Paul's imprisonment.

Question 11. This question is designed to help people relate Paul's example to their immediate circumstances. Be ready to model this for the group by sharing how you plan to face a specific difficulty. This sharing can very naturally lead into a time of prayer.

Study 4. The Path of Humility. Philippians 2:1-18.

Purpose: Philippians 2:6-11 is one of the best-loved passages of the Bible because of its beautiful and poetic description of Christ's humility. When read in the context of the entire passage, it teaches that the humble service of Christ is to be an example for all Christian living.

Question 4. Jesus' humility is shown in what he willingly gave up. The phrase "did not consider equality with God something to be grasped" teaches that, although he possessed the "very nature" of God, he did not demand his rights as God. Jesus could have appeared as the ruler of the universe instead of as its savior, thereby receiving all the recognition that was due him. Instead, Jesus gave up all rights and came as a servant.

Question 7. God rewarded Christ's humility by exalting him in glory. It has been suggested that verses 14-16 teach that when we humble ourselves, God will also exalt us. What do you think?

Question 8. We can think of the words *work out* (v. 12) in the same way that we would work out in a gym. God has given us salvation. Now it is our job to work out or exercise that salvation in the real world just as we should exercise the muscles God gave us. At the same time, God "works in" us to complete what he has begun.

Paul seems to use the phrase *with fear and trembling* to express a humble frame of mind. For other examples of this phrase, see 1 Corinthians 2:3, 2 Corinthians 7:15 and Ephesians 6:5.

Question 10. Some members of your group may be uncomfortable with the word *boast.* It is true that some versions substitute *proud,* but the force of the Greek is much stronger than this. Consider Webster's definition of boast: "to glory in having or doing something."

Question 12. Spend time praying for the plans each person has made.

Study 5. Servants of Christ. Philippians 2:19-30.

Purpose: Christian service is the main theme of this study. The previous study considered Christ's example of humility. This passage gives us several human examples in the lives of Timothy, Epaphroditus, Paul and the Philippians.

Question 2. Timothy is being sent as Paul's envoy and representative. His mission will be a powerful follow-up to the concerns of Paul's letter.

Questions 4-5. These questions combine interpretation and application. Before the group can properly answer question 4, they must think about the needs of the church: What are Christ's interests and concerns for the church? How might Timothy have demonstrated his concern for the welfare of the church? Question 5 then helps the group to think about how they might follow Timothy's example in their own church or fellowship group.

Question 6. Why was Epaphroditus homesick? Some scholars believe that he was a leader in the Philippian church and felt a pastoral responsibility for his congregation. Others suggest that he yearned to stand beside his brothers and sisters through a time of persecution. Paul was afraid that Epaphroditus might be criticized for returning and that the Philippians might conclude their mission had failed. Therefore, Paul clearly states that the return was his idea. Paul also gives a glowing commendation of Epaphroditus to put a stop to any criticism. Epaphroditus was to be welcomed back with joy and honor as a missionary who had completed his task. The exact nature of his sickness is a mystery.

Question 8. Your group may want to write a thank-you note to a staff worker, pastor, missionary or other leader as a way of showing that person honor. Or you might honor the person with a party, phone call or special event.

Study 6. Rejoice in the Lord. Philippians 3:1-21.

Purpose: The purpose of this study is to learn that joy does not come through legalistic attempts to become self-righteous but rather through knowing Jesus Christ, pressing on toward our heavenly goal and setting our minds on heavenly things.

Question 3. The people Paul is describing were known as Judaizers and believed all Christians should live strictly by the Jewish laws and customs. Notice how Paul satirically calls these people "dogs" in verse 2. *Dogs* was a derogatory title used by orthodox Jews to describe Gentiles, whom they saw as God's enemies. By this switch of terms, Paul points out that it is the Judaizers and not the Gentiles who are God's enemies. *Mutilators of the flesh* refers to the Jewish law of circumcision.

Question 9. The group will probably need help with this question, since verses 10-11 are difficult to interpret. Paul describes in greater detail what is involved in knowing Christ.

The power of his resurrection does not just refer to the power that raised Christ from the dead. It also refers to the power of the resurrected Christ, who is at work in the life of every believer.

The fellowship of sharing in his sufferings does not mean that Paul's suffering would somehow complete the atoning work of Christ. Yet Paul realized that every true follower of Jesus would experience suffering. Jesus said, "If they persecuted me, they will persecute you also" (Jn 15:20).

Paul's desire was also to become "like him in his death." Tradition tells us that Paul did experience martyrdom outside Rome. But every Christian is to take up his or her cross and follow Jesus, whether it results in death or not.

Verse 11, in some translations, gives the impression that Paul was uncertain whether or not he would be raised from the dead. Instead of "if possible" (RSV) the NIV has "somehow," which better captures Paul's meaning. He is not uncertain about his own resurrection but rather the events leading to it.

Question 12. Scholars disagree as to whom Paul is talking about in these verses. Some believe he is referring to the Judaizers mentioned earlier in the chapter. Others believe he is talking about a group of Gentiles who insisted on living as they please. Although it may seem as if no two groups could be further apart, they are both guilty of the same thing—their heart is set on worldly things.

Study 7. Stand Firm in the Lord. Philippians 4:1-9.
Purpose: How can Christians be sure that they will remain firm in their faith as the years pass by? This study is designed to help people consider and act upon Paul's advice for standing firm in the Lord.

Questions 3-4. The word *crown* was commonly used to denote a wreath awarded to the victor of an athletic contest. Paul regarded the Philippians as just such a reward. They were his seal of apostleship and the proof that his labor had been used by God. They would be his crown at the final day (R. P. Martin, *The Epistle of Paul to the Philippians* [Grand Rapids, Mich.: Eerdmans, 1959] p. 165).

Question 5. Women were apparently quite influential in the Philippian church. We know from Acts 16 that the first convert was a woman. From this passage we learn that Euodia and Syntyche had worked at Paul's side in proclaiming the gospel. Therefore, the quarrel between these women was all the worse because of their influence on others.

Question 6. A yokefellow is a companion or partner. It is unclear whom Paul is referring to as "loyal yokefellow." Some suggest that Paul is talking to someone who knows he has this gift and responsibility. Others believe that *syzygos* (Greek for *yokefellow*) is a proper name which just happens to be very fitting. A third option is that Paul is putting out a general call for someone to take the role of yokefellow.

Question 11. After the group discusses how such thoughts can help us, it might be good to think of specific things we might think of during anxious times. For example, what thoughts might have helped you during your most recent period of anxiety?

Question 12. If we practice what we have learned in this passage, we will have not only the peace of God (v. 7) but also the God of peace (v. 9) with us. What a promise!

Study 8. Paul's Thank-You Note. Philippians 4:10-23.

Purpose: This passage teaches that missions-giving is of greater benefit to the giver than the receiver. Therefore, the study should prompt people toward greater support of missions.

Question 4. "*Giving and receiving* refers to a double transaction. Material gifts, passed from the church to the apostle, and spiritual blessings flowed the other way" (Martin, *Philippians,* pp. 179-80).

Question 8. Paul wants the Philippians to know that his dependence is on God alone. Too often people think of missionaries as charity cases who are unable to make it on their own. With this attitude, missions-giving becomes an act of pity rather than what it really is—an investment in God's kingdom.

Question 9. The group may wish to discuss how to decide how much to give and to whom to give it. The book *How to Give Away Your Money* by Simon Webley (IVP, 1978) and the booklet *The Graduated*

Tithe by Ronald Sider (IVP, 1978) would be helpful in such a discussion.

Study 9. Putting It All Together. Philippians 1—4.

Purpose: After studying each passage in its individual context, your group needs to step back and see how the major themes flow through the book. The purpose of this study is to tie together the themes of Philippians. Group members should be reminded of the issues they have confronted and leave with the feeling, "Now I know what Philippians is about and how it applies to my life."

Question 2. You can ask members to skim through the book looking for references to *joy* and *rejoice,* or you can assign the verses listed to the various members of the group and have them report on what they find. If your group is using the Revised Standard Version, you will find that 1:18b is numbered as 1:19.

Donald Baker, a former staff member with Inter-Varsity Christian Fellowship, is pastor of Grace Reformed Church in Waterloo, Iowa.